the big pile of dirt

by eleanor clymer

illustrated by robert shore

HOLT, RINEHART AND WINSTON   new york   chicago   san francisco

books by eleanor clymer

THE BIG PILE OF DIRT

MY BROTHER STEVIE

WHEELS

SEARCH FOR A LIVING FOSSIL

the big pile of dirt

On our street there was an empty lot. It was small, but it was full of junk. There was an armchair with the stuffing coming out. There was an old mattress. There were bottles and automobile tires and other things that people didn't want. And in the middle was a big pile of dirt. But I better not start telling you about that yet. First I will tell how we got started with the lot. It was like this.

See, we live in this old building. There's me. My name is Mike. I'm the oldest in my family. I have a sister Arleen, and two brothers, twins, five years old. Their names are Billy and Sam. After school Arleen minds them, when my mother is working. I have to help her sometimes, when they act up.

I have some friends that live in the building. My two best friends are Joe and Russ. We go to school together and we're on the basketball team. After school we go someplace and play.

That's where the trouble started. There wasn't any place to play. We couldn't all play in somebody's apartment. There's no room. The apartments have too much stuff in them—beds and things.

If we played ball in the street, the little kids would run out after the ball. They could get killed that way. When Arleen tells them not to, they don't listen to her. They listen to me all right, but I can't mind them all the time.

If we played on the stoop, somebody would come out and say, "You kids get off that stoop, you're blocking the door."

If we played handball, they said, "No handball against that wall." They put up a sign, no ball playing allowed.

Sometimes we went up on the roof. It was nice there. You felt high up, close to the sky. You could see the tall buildings way downtown, and the boats on the river and the Ferris wheel over on the other side. You could see white birds flying around. I liked to watch them.

But there's this lady, Mrs. Crane, her laundry got stolen once. So after that they made us get off the roof.

"All right, you kids go on down now, this is no place for you." So we had to go down, even if Mrs. Crane was sitting there watching her laundry.

And besides, it was no place for Billy and Sam. They might fall off. Let's face it, I couldn't get rid of those kids. Arleen couldn't handle them.

There was a good place in the hall behind the stairs. I went there a few times with Joe and Russ and we played cards. But Billy fell down and cut his head, and Arleen came running for me, and the kids were yelling, and the Super came out of his apartment and said, "What's going on here? All you kids, out!"

We played in the upstairs hall. But Mrs. Casey, who lives in 4D, the minute she hears a sound she pops her head out and says, "No playing in the hall." We certainly couldn't hurt the hall, the floor is all broken already, but never mind.

Then we played in the side court. But Mrs. Giotto, she lives in 2A on that side, she was mad at us because we laughed at her, because she was fishing. I'm not fooling. She really was. See, it was a windy day, and she had some towels or something on a line outside her window, and they blew down. And she leaned out of the window with a ball of string and

a fishhook and let down the hook and fished one of them up, and when she let down the hook again we put an old sock on it. She was a fat lady and she looked pretty funny fishing out the window especially when she saw the sock. We couldn't help laughing. So then she was mad at us, and always told us to get out of the court.

Once we went down to the furnace room. It was warm there, and the furnace was like a monster with one big eye and a mouth full of fire. It was scary, but nice. But it was no use. The Super came and said, "This is no place for you."

We had to find a place. And it had to be a place where all of us could go. That's the only way I would have any peace.

Well, right next to our house there was another house. Nobody lived in it, because it wasn't safe. It was all ready to fall down, and the doors and windows were covered with boards. One day some men came with trucks and knocked it down. We all stood around and watched. They kept telling us to get away, but we kept coming back.

They put up boards like big wooden shelves to stand on, and the men climbed up and knocked pieces out of the walls. You could see inside

where the bedrooms were, painted pink and blue. You could see the stairs and the kitchens and bathrooms.

They took it all away, and I guess they dumped it somewhere. I wondered if the people that used to live there knew that their house was in a dump somewhere.

Well, when they got through there was nothing left but an empty lot with some bricks and old boards in it. Then it started to get full of junk. People would throw things in it, broken dishes and bottles and cans, and all the things people don't want. Or else they would come out at night when they thought nobody was looking. They put this old armchair out there, and automobile tires, and a great big old can, and other stuff.

Every day my friends and I would go and see what was there. We used to look for treasure, and we found some good things. I found a hammer that the men left. And Johnny was lucky, he found an old baby carriage with four good wheels. He made a scooter with the wheels, and the girls played with the carriage.

This was in summer, so we played there all day. Joe and Russ and I made a fort out of bricks. We played we were shooting flaming arrows at it, only we didn't really. We had to be careful on account of the little kids. Arleen had to watch that the twins didn't get hurt with the broken glass and nails. Her friend Margie came with her little sister and she would put things in her mouth if you didn't look out.

But still it was a pretty good place. We made a swing for the little kids out of an old tire. We hung it from some posts we drove in the ground.

And all the time we were waiting for somebody to tell us to get out, but nobody did. Even our Super didn't pay any attention to us. But what happened was something else.

One day when we were playing, some ladies came. They came in a car with a man, and they all got out and stood looking at our lot. We watched them, and heard what they said.

One lady said, "This is a mess. Look at all that broken glass and junk."

Another lady said, "That is no place for these children. They ought to be sent out of there."

A third lady said, "How can we have a beautiful city with places like this? Mr. Mayor, you must do something."

I thought to myself, "Could that be the Mayor?" And I got ready for him to chase us out.

But he didn't. He just said, "Yes, ladies, you are right. I will give orders for something to be done." Then they went away.

Joe said, "Now what? Will they make us get out?"

"No," I said, "they just want to clean it up."

Arleen said, "That means we get out. I knew it."

"Well, wait and see," I said. But I was afraid she was right and I would have to find a new place.

But that is not what happened. Something different happened. One day a truck came. It was a very big truck and it was full of dirt. Two men got out. They stood and looked at our empty lot. They scratched their heads.

One said, "Is this the place, Mac?"

The other said, "Yep. This is it."

The first one said, "We're supposed to deliver this dirt here?"

The other said, "Yep, those are the orders."

The first one said, "Okay, let her go."

They backed up the truck on to
our lot. Then they let her go. They
dumped all that dirt right in the
middle of our lot. It made a roar like
thunder. Then they went away.

Joe asked me, "What's it all about?"

I said, "It beats me. I don't know."

We waited for something else to
happen. But nothing happened. I
went and stuck my hand in the dirt.
It was nice and soft. It was clean
dirt. It seemed like they wanted to
give us a present. I thought we might
as well enjoy it.

So I said, "Come on, kids."

Then we started playing. We climbed up the big pile of dirt. I stood on top and said, "I am the President." Joe came behind me and gave me a shove. I sat down and slid to the bottom.

Then we started digging. We had no shovels but we got some pieces of board and some cans to dig with. The little kids were busy filling up old pots and dishes with dirt and making cakes. I and Joe and Russ, we hadn't dug in the dirt for a long time, but we did it, too, just like the little kids. It was fun.

The girls played supermarket. They put a board across some bricks for a counter. They filled up cans with dirt and made believe to sell them. It was funny the way they talked.

"How much for the beans, Mrs. Jones?"

"Two cans for a quarter."

"That's too high. Everything is too high these days."

You sure could do a lot of things with that dirt. We didn't go home till it got nearly dark.

The next day we went back. I was almost afraid to go. I thought the dirt would be gone. But it was there.

I had a great idea. I found a garbage can cover. I climbed to the top and slid down. Pretty soon all the kids were sliding down. They got a little wild. Johnny and Pete got in a fight and started throwing dirt. But I said, "No throwing dirt. You could get it in your eyes. That's an order." So then nobody threw dirt.

My little brother Billy, he's the one that's so wild and is always getting hurt, he piled dirt inside an old tire. Then he got in himself and sat there. "This is my boat," he said, and he sat there for hours.

Sam found a dead pigeon. The girls screamed, but I said, "We can have a funeral." So the girls brought flowers that they found in an ash can. After the funeral they planted the flowers in the dirt, and Margie said, "This is going to be like a park. Don't pick the flowers."

Arleen said, "If it's a park there should be benches for people to sit while they mind the kids." So the girls made benches out of old boards. Joe and I had a better idea. We dragged the old armchair up to the top of the pile and took turns sitting in it.

I said, "Whoever is the President can sit in it." So every day another kid was President. He could sit in the chair and give orders.

One day when I was President, two of the kids started throwing stuff at the dirt. They threw rocks to see how far in they would go. Then one of them threw a piece of glass.

I said, "Quit that. No glass in the dirt. Somebody could be digging with their hands and get cut."

So they didn't do it any more. After all, it was our dirt.

Then one day it rained. I thought, "Now it will be all mud and wash away." But it wasn't. It was like sand. The water sort of ran through it

and left it a little wet. It was better than ever. You could shape things out of it. I made a man's head and stuck an old hat on it.

We started making houses in the dirt. We made streets and walls. It was like a city. Some kids brought toy cars and trucks and ran them in the streets.

Well, we kept waiting for something to happen to our pile of dirt, but nothing did, so we forgot. We just thought about it as if it was ours.

It got to be winter, and the dirt got hard as rock. We played we were mountain climbers. Then it snowed. It was swell for sliding down. We built a snow man on top.

Then spring came and it got warm. One day Margie started to yell, "Look! Stuff is growing!"

We looked, and there was green grass on one side of the dirt.

Margie said, "Don't touch it, you kids. Keep off the grass." The kids took care not to step on Margie's grass.

Then Arleen said, "We ought to have trees." But where could we get trees?

One day Johnny found a can of paint. He painted trees on the wall of the building next to the lot. It looked good. It was almost too good to be true, which is what my mother says sometimes.

Well, one day when we were playing, a car stopped, and some ladies got out. A man was with them, the same Mayor.

I said to the kids, "Hide, quick." So we hid and watched. The ladies looked at our pile of dirt. One of them got mad.

She said, "Mr. Mayor, you promised to have this place cleaned up, but nothing has been done."

The Mayor said, "Yes, I remember. I gave orders to clean it up but somebody delivered a pile of dirt instead by mistake. I bet somebody else is still waiting for that pile of dirt."

Another lady said, "Those children are still playing there. It should not be allowed. It is dangerous."

The Mayor said, "Yes, you are right. We will have it cleaned up and a fence put around it."

Joe whispered, "Are they going to take away our pile of dirt?"

Arleen said, "They can't."

Two little kids started to cry.

I said, "Keep still, you kids. Let me think." The ladies were pointing at our stuff and arguing. The Mayor kept shaking his head. I thought, "I have to do something."

Then before I could think any more, I marched out. I felt as if somebody was pushing me, only nobody was. I walked right in front of them and I said, "Excuse me but please leave our stuff alone."

They all looked surprised. The Mayor said, "What's this? Who are you?"

I said, "I'm just one of the kids. This is our pile of dirt. We play here. Please don't take it away."

The Mayor said, "Is it all right if we look at it?"

I said, "Sure." So they went in the lot and looked at all the stuff we had there.

The Mayor said, "You see, children, we want to clean this place up."

I said, "We like it this way." I was awfully scared, I thought maybe he could arrest me for talking like that. But I had to say it. I thought, "They are going to take it away from us, and there is nothing we can do. There is nobody to help us."

But all of a sudden we heard a voice. "What is the matter? Did the kids do something?"

We all looked up and it was Mrs. Giotto, leaning out of her window. She said, "Wait, I'll be right down." She slammed the window and in a minute she was down. She had her apron on, and flour on her hands, as if she was making ravioli.

She said, "Those kids are not bothering anybody, you leave them alone."

I sure was surprised. She wasn't mad at us after all! The Mayor and the ladies were surprised, too.

One lady said, "But don't you see, this is dangerous."

Mrs. Giotto said, "Nobody got hurt here yet. Those kids have no place to play. You should leave them alone."

Suddenly we heard another voice. "Yes, she's right. The children need a place to play." It was Mrs. Casey from 4D.

Then another lady came out of the building and said, "The children were getting along fine here."

Then the Super came out. He said, "Since they have that dirt they don't bother anybody. It's a good thing for them."

Then I saw my mother coming home from work. When she saw the crowd she got scared and ran to us. "What happened?" she asked. "Was there an accident?"

Arleen said, "We're all right, Mama, but they want to clean up our pile of dirt."

Mama said, "Clean it up? What for? It's all right the way it is."

And suddenly I thought, "What do you know! They're on our side! They're fighting for us!"

The Mayor looked at us standing there. Then he looked at his ladies. And then he smiled all over his face.

He said, "You know what? I have a great idea. We'll make a park here for the kids."

Then all the grown-ups began to smile, too, and nod their heads, and Mrs. Giotto said, "Now you're talking."

The Mayor said, "We'll clean it up and put in benches and swings and things to climb on. How would you like that, children?"

We stood there and couldn't say a word. It was too sudden. But Billy spoke up. He said, "What about our pile of dirt?"

The Mayor said, "Well, I don't know. It's hard to keep a pile of dirt clean. It gets all over everything."

Then I got brave and said, "We don't care. We like it." And all the other kids nodded their heads yes.

So the Mayor thought a while and then he said, "I tell you what. We'll move the pile of dirt over to one side and put some fresh dirt on. We'll build a little fence around it, and you can still have it. And we'll make a wading pool for you to wade and sail boats. How's that?"

It was our turn to think a while. Then Margie said, "What about the grass on the pile?" And Johnny said, "What about the painting on the wall?"

The Mayor said, "We could move the grass over, or we could give you some seeds to plant new grass. And we'll keep the painting. We could even give you more paint and you could paint the rest of the wall."

So we said okay.

Well, the next week the men got to work. They cleaned it all up.

They had a bulldozer move the dirt into the back of the lot. Some of us got a ride on it.

They built a pool, and they put benches and swings, just like they said, and they put concrete pipes to crawl through, and big concrete animals to climb on, with hollow places underneath where you could just sit and think if you wanted to. They planted bushes and flowers, and Margie put a little fence around her grass and even planted her own flowers.

And we painted the walls. We made palm trees and lions and mountains and all kinds of stuff.

It is a very good park, and everybody is proud of it. All the people on our block came to a party, and they take care of it and don't throw junk in the park, but keep it clean. We sure needed that park.

But sometimes I go there by myself, real early in the morning, or when it has just rained, or in winter, because that's when there aren't so many other people around. And I make believe. I pretend it's the way it used to be, just a big pile of dirt in the middle of an empty lot.

ELEANOR CLYMER was born in New York City. She attended Columbia and New York Universities and Bank Street College and is a graduate of the University of Wisconsin. She is the author of more than thirty-five books for children including *My Brother Stevie* and *Search for a Living Fossil*. Though a city-dweller most of her life, Mrs. Clymer now lives in Katonah, New York, in the hills of northern Westchester. She writes affectionately about the city, but loves the country, too, and finds that city and country children are alike in many ways, and have the same needs and feelings.

ROBERT SHORE was educated at the Cranbrook Academy of Art in Michigan. A distinguished artist who is exhibited widely, he was awarded a Fulbright Fellowship in painting in 1952. His illustrations have also appeared in magazines and books—he was honored by the Society of Illustrators with the Gold Medal in 1966—but *The Big Pile of Dirt* is his first picture book. Born and raised in New York City, Mr. Shore is well-versed in the problems of urban life and aware of the special dilemma of children with no place to play. His feeling of involvement is reflected in the sensitive, expressionistic paintings. Mr. Shore is married and the father of two children and is an instructor at the School of Visual Arts.

THE BOOK was printed by offset; display type is Palatino Semi Bold, lower case, and text type is Linotype Janson. Robert Shore's illustrations are casein paintings.